Double It Daily

Lalie Harcourt & Ricki Wortzman

Illustrated by Farida Zaman

 Dominie Press, Inc.

I could spend my life at the fair. I love the rides and the balloons.
I love the games and the prizes. But most of all, I love…

2

…the cotton candy!

    Today the woman who sells cotton candy gave me a job. The best part is that she's paying me in cotton candy! Look at my contract.

CONTRACT

The pay for this job is in cotton candy.

First day's pay is one bag.

Each day after the first day, pay is doubled.

Signed

_____ and _____

Today, I earned **1** bag of candy.

On my second day of work, I helped clean the machine.

The day went by quickly. Before I knew it, I was on my way home. I was paid 2 bags of cotton candy, because when you double 1 you get 2. I ate 1 bag before I got home. I ate the other bag after supper.

My third day at work was a lot like the second, but there were a lot
more people. I was so busy, I didn't have time to eat any cotton candy.
At the end of the day I was paid 4 bags, because when you double
2 you get 4. Of course, you probably think that I ate some on my
way home. You're right! I also had some after supper and before bed.

There is no such thing as too much cotton candy.

On my fourth day of work, it rained all day. The time went by very slowly. Not many people feel like going to the fair in the rain, but my boss said, "A deal is a deal."

She paid me 8 bags of cotton candy, because when you double 4 you get 8. My boss even let me go home early.

Now, 8 bags is a lot of cotton candy. I gave some to my brothers and sisters. Everyone seemed happy about my new job.

On my fifth day at work, my boss made the cotton candy. I took people's money and gave them change. You can make a lot of money selling cotton candy! There are lots of people just like me — people who love cotton candy.

I hadn't really thought about how many bags I would be taking home until my boss gave me 16 bags and said, "See you tomorrow."

Well, when you double 8 you get 16, so my boss was right.

That night just about everyone on my street had some cotton candy.

On the sixth day, I took my little brother's wagon with me to work. I had thought about how much cotton candy I would be paid. I figured out that when you double 16 you get 32.

I knew that 32 bags would be a lot to carry. I was right! They filled the wagon. No one was very interested in having any cotton candy that night. Even I didn't want any. So, I stuffed it into my closet and went to sleep.

The seventh day of work was very hot and very busy. The time flew by, and before I knew it I was getting paid. I was glad that my mom was driving me home, because when you double 32 you get 64. That was the number of cotton candy bags I had to take with me. They filled the back of the car.

At home, my brothers and sisters helped me carry the bags to my room. I stared at those bags for a long time. Then I knew that you can have too much cotton candy.

I did some math on my way to work the next day.
I knew that when you double 64 you get 128.
I knew that when you double 128 you get 256.
Double 256 and you get 512! I kept doubling numbers
in my head.

When I saw my boss I said, "I'd like to talk to you.
I really don't want to be paid in cotton candy anymore.
Can you pay me in pennies?"